REAL LIVES

Harriet
Tubman

D1615643

REAL LIVES

Harriet
Tubman

Deborah Chancellor

A & C BLACK
AN IMPRINT OF BLOOMSBURY
LONDON   NEW DELHI   NEW YORK   SYDNEY

For Matthew, Harry, Edward and Imogen

First published 2013 by
A & C Black, an imprint of Bloomsbury Publishing Plc
50 Bedford Square, London, WC1B 3DP

www.bloomsbury.com

ISBN 978-1-4081-7839-3

A CIP catalogue for this book is available from the British Library.

Printed and bound by CPI Group (UK) Ltd, Croydon CR0 4YY

1 3 5 7 9 10 8 6 4 2

Contents

Author's Note

This account of the life of Harriet Tubman contains passages of dialogue between Harriet and some of the people she knew. The style of speech has been modified, both to simplify the plantation dialect spoken by many slaves during this period, and to avoid the strong racist language often used by white people at the time.

1
Ship of Death : 1770s

'Look over there – I'd swear there's one of them hiding in those trees. I just saw a branch move.'

A young man stepped forward into the dappled sunlight, wiping his sweaty face with a dirty cloth. It was the end of a long day's hunting in the African rainforest, and he just wanted to give up and start the trek back to camp.

'Haven't we caught enough for today?' he whispered back to his companion. 'We've got our quota, and the ship sails at dawn tomorrow.'

'So many die on the way,' came the older man's reply. 'If you ask me, you can never have enough.'

Above their heads, a small eight-year-old girl gripped tightly on to the scaly bark of a young teak tree. She heard the two men talking, but their unfamiliar words were like the chatter of monkeys.

Why didn't I listen to Mother? she thought. *She warned me not to stray from the village.*

Too late now, she remembered the tales she had been told about white men who crept into the forest to steal people away. Panic rose up in her chest and she began to feel dizzy.

A thin, buzzing sound broke the silence. A mosquito landed on the girl's arm and prepared to draw blood. Instinctively, she moved to flick it away, and the small shift in movement upset her balance. She grabbed on to a branch to steady herself and the rustle of leaves caught the hunters' attention.

'I was right,' cried the older man with a grim laugh. In one deft movement, he pulled the girl down to the ground and twisted her arm behind her back. He held her firmly as she flailed like a trapped bird. Too frightened to scream, the girl could feel the forest closing in around her.

'Let's go back to camp now,' the young man said, impatiently. 'I can't wait to get out of here tomorrow. I've had enough of this godforsaken place.'

As the girl struggled to break free, she saw a group of men, women and children standing in the shadows, bound together in chains. She scanned their faces, but didn't recognize anyone.

They are from another tribe, she thought. *What's going to become of us all?*

The captives were forced to walk for hours through the dense rainforest, until finally there was a change in the smell of the air. A slight breeze rippled, tasting fresh on the girl's dry tongue. She had never travelled this far from her village before, and as she stumbled over a ridge, she gasped in amazement at what she saw: a vast expanse of water, stretching out towards the distant horizon. She had heard about the sea, but had never seen it with her own eyes. The huge red sun was sinking into the water and a tall ship was silhouetted against the riot of colours in the sky.

Some of the people around her began to wail, falling to their knees in the fine white sand. They did not yet know the full horror of what lay ahead, but terrified and exhausted, they understood that their suffering had only just begun.

At dawn, the first rays of light spread over the leafy canopy of the rainforest. The captives were led down the beach and on to the ship. They had spent the night crammed together with many others in a fortified prison by the shore. The girl had managed an hour of shattered sleep, leaning up against a woman who had not stopped sobbing the whole night long.

As the wretched prisoners boarded the ship, the girl watched the crew beat anyone who did not follow their orders. The captives were stripped naked, then split into groups of men, women and children and bound together in different parts of the ship's hold. They were packed so tightly, it was impossible to move, let alone try to escape.

'That's five hundred and fifty on board,' called one of the ship's crew, as he finished a final head count. 'Time to set sail. Tell the captain it's anchors aweigh.'

It was the mid-1770s, and the international slave trade was at its peak. The tall ship was one of many thousands to make its way from Africa's west coast across the Atlantic to the east coast of America. The young girl was a member of the Ashanti tribe, from an area of rainforest in a country now called Ghana. She was just one of countless men, women and children to be snatched from her homeland, transported halfway across the world, and sold as a slave to an American plantation owner.

The long weeks of the voyage dragged by. The captives on board were given just enough food and water to stay alive, and were brutally punished for any sign of defiance. As the Ashanti girl lay in darkness, shackled to her neighbour on a dirty wooden pallet, she tried not to think about her family, but their faces were etched in her memory.

I'll never see them again, she thought. *And I didn't even get to say goodbye.*

The miserable conditions in the galley got worse with every day that passed. The slaves were cooped up like animals, and disease became rife. The stench below deck was overpowering and the rancid air was thick with sickness and death. The Ashanti girl listened to the groans all around her – only occasionally did she hear a few words of her own language. One night, the little boy next to her grabbed her hand, his eyes wide with fear. The Ashanti girl didn't need to understand what he was saying to know he was dying from a fever. She squeezed his hot, clammy fingers and sang him a lullaby that her grandmother used to sing. The next morning, the boy's hand was cold. A member of the crew unlocked his chains and carried him away.

They'll throw him overboard, the Ashanti girl thought. *Perhaps he's the lucky one. At least his pain is over now. Who knows what lies ahead for me?*

* * *

After three, endless months at sea, the ship finally docked in the calm waters of Chesapeake Bay, on the eastern shore of Maryland, in America. The bright sunlight danced on the waves as they lapped at the ship's bow. It was hard for anyone strolling along the quayside to imagine the carnage that lay hidden below deck.

The slaves were led one by one off the ship, and the Ashanti girl stumbled down the gangplank on to the busy dock. She stood up straight, holding her head high. She was proud, and refused to be defeated by her fate. Blinking at the dazzling sunlight, she made herself a promise. *I'll never give up*, she vowed.

She was taken with some other slaves to a large

holding pen, where she was scrubbed clean and checked over for disease. Then, like an animal, she was branded to mark her as a slave. As the hot metal was pressed into her skin, a searing pain shot through her small, thin body. She had barely recovered when a woman with rough hands grabbed her and smeared stinking grease over her face and limbs, in an attempt to make her look healthy.

The slave dealers appeared to be in a hurry. The Ashanti girl was herded together with a group of other women and children, then pushed into the back of a horse-drawn cart. Several carts pulled away together, beginning the bumpy drive to a nearby town.

'We mustn't be late for the auction today,' muttered the driver at the front of the convoy, whipping his horses to make them go faster.

At the slave market, a crowd of plantation owners were gathered together, keen to examine the slaves for sale.

'Let's hope the quality's up to scratch!' said one man to his friend, as the slave carts rumbled in to the square. There was a shortage of labour in this state, where the soil was fertile and there was plenty of land to farm, so plantation owners were willing to pay well for new slaves. The men chatted and joked in the sunshine as the slaves were led towards one side of the market square.

Before the bidding began, the prospective buyers were permitted to give the auction lots a close inspection. One by one, the slaves stood on the auction block and were prodded and poked. Their mouths were prised open and their teeth were checked for signs of rot. One plantation owner, a man called Atthow Pattison, was especially fussy about his slaves.

'I like to get my money's worth,' he quipped to the auctioneer. 'Any slave of mine must be healthy enough to work on my land, but handsome enough to serve in my home.'

The Ashanti slave caught Pattison's attention. She had a spirited expression and was not afraid to look him in the eye. To her advantage, she was young and strong, which would make her a good investment.

She'll work hard, and any children she has one day will belong to me, Pattison thought approvingly.

The auction got underway and Pattison made a successful bid for the Ashanti girl. He paid his money, then rode back to his plantation, near Bucktown in Dorchester County, Maryland. When he showed his new property off to his wife, Pattison could see that she was pleased with his choice.

'We should call her "Modesty",' Mrs Pattison suggested, 'and hope she lives up to her name.'

In that moment, the Ashanti girl's true African name and heritage disappeared forever. She was a slave now, someone else's property, with no rights of her own.

2

Born into
Slavery: 1797

'Ma, you must come up to the big house at once!'
cried a tall, slender girl of about fourteen, tugging
impatiently at her mother's sleeve. Modesty was
drawing water from the well and her daughter's
sudden clamour made her drop the bucket with a
splash. She stood up, rubbing her stiff back.

'What is it, Rit?' she said, looking wearily at her
daughter. She felt the usual mixture of love and
anger as she contemplated her pale-skinned child.
Love, because Modesty's daughter Rit shared
the blood of her ancestors back in Africa. Anger,
because she also shared the blood of her father and
slave master, Atthow Pattison.

'Look at that baby,' people had gossiped when

Rit was born. 'That's a white man's child for sure. How does Mrs Pattison bear the shame?'

Modesty's situation was not exactly unique. Plantation owners often fathered children by their slaves. These illegitimate children would grow up to serve their half-brothers and sisters in their father's household.

Rit dragged her daydreaming mother back to the present.

'It's Master Pattison, Ma!' cried Rit. 'They say he's dying!'

Modesty wiped her hands on her skirts and ran with Rit up the dusty path to the house. Standing in the doorway was Mary Pattison, Atthow's granddaughter. She was just a few years older than Rit.

'You're too late – he's already slipped away,' said Mary. She looked Rit up and down.

'You need to know that my grandfather left Rit to me in his will,' she said to Modesty, brusquely. 'Your daughter belongs to me now.'

Mary was engaged to a local plantation owner called Joseph Brodess, and would soon leave the Pattison plantation to live with her new husband, taking Rit with her. Modesty would not cry over the death of her master, but losing Rit... that was a different matter. The tears began to prick behind her eyes.

'Be good to her, Miss Mary,' Modesty whispered. 'She's all I've got in the world.'

* * *

After the wedding, Rit went to live with Mary on her husband's plantation. When Mary had her first child, Rit nursed the baby, a little boy called Edward Brodess. But soon after the birth, the baby's father died and Mary, now a widow, had to marry again. Once again she moved with her slaves to her new husband's plantation.

One Sunday, Rit was given a few hours off to visit her mother. She told Modesty her news.

'I've moved again, Ma,' she said. 'My new master, Anthony Thompson, is just like all the rest. I don't know what Miss Mary sees in him.'

Modesty felt anxiety gnaw away at her stomach like a cancer. 'Keep away from him, child,' she warned. Rit was looking radiant that day – her skin was glowing and her eyes were shining bright. Now Rit lived apart from her mother, Modesty was powerless to protect her beautiful sixteen-year-old daughter from the unwanted advances of her new master.

'I've something else to tell you, Ma,' said Rit, interrupting her mother's dark thoughts. 'Master Thompson has many slaves, and his marriage to Miss Mary has brought our two households together. One of Master Thompson's slaves is sweet on me, and I'm growing fond of him, too. He's the master's favourite – he manages Thompson's forests over in Peters Neck.'

Modesty smiled at the look of innocent happiness on her daughter's face.

'What's his name, Rit?' she asked.

'Ben,' replied Rit. 'Ben Ross. He's the one for me, Ma, I just know it.'

Modesty embraced her daughter.

'I hope you are very happy together,' she laughed.

Rit and Ben got permission to marry, and in 1808, when Rit was about eighteen, she had her first child, a baby girl called Linah. Both parents had been born into slavery; and Linah too faced a life of servitude. As they gazed at their vulnerable daughter, they feared for her future.

'Will she ever be free?' they asked themselves. But their tiny baby's fate was out of their hands.

Rit and Ben's family grew quickly. By 1815, they had four young children. This was excellent news for their master Anthony Thompson.

'Those slave children are valuable assets,' he told his stepson Edward. 'I can always sell them, if I'm short of cash.' Like all slave families, Rit and Ben were well aware that they could be separated from each other, and their children, without a moment's notice.

The fifth child in Ben and Rit's family was a little girl, born in around 1822. Like her older brothers and sisters, the baby was born at Thompson's plantation, in an area called Peters Neck.

'Let's call her... Araminta,' said Rit, cradling her tiny newborn in her arms.

'That's a big mouthful for such a small one,' said Ben, chuckling. 'She can be "Minty", for short.'

The nickname stuck. It was only when Minty grew up and got married that she chose a more serious and grown-up name for herself. She gave herself her mother Rit's full name, *Harriet*.

Harriet's earliest memory was a sad one. One evening, when she was just a toddler, she came across her mother Rit, weeping inconsolably in the cabin. Her father Ben was trying to comfort her.

'I can't bear it,' sobbed Rit.

'Hush now my love,' soothed Ben. 'We'll get through this, just you see.'

'What's happened, Ma?' asked Linah, Harriet's oldest sister, who was now seventeen years old.

'It's Master Edward,' said Ben, answering for his distraught wife. 'He turned twenty-one today, so he has inherited all his mother's property. That means you, all your brothers and sisters, and your mother too. You all belong to Master Edward now.'

'What about you, Pa?' asked Linah. But she already knew the answer.

'I still belong to Anthony Thompson – your mother and I now have different masters. Edward Brodess doesn't own me.'

'But why is Ma so upset?' persisted Linah.

'Master Edward announced today that he's moving to his mother's old plantation, and he's taking all of his *property* with him,' explained Ben. A deep frown line creased his brow. 'He wants to make his own way in the world. That means you're all going with him, but I'll have to stay here.'

21

A flood of sadness washed over the slave cabin. Harriet's face crumpled and she began to howl. Ben picked her up and swung her in the air.

'Be brave like the rest of us, little Minty,' he said. 'I want you to look after your mother for me.' Harriet hiccupped and stopped crying at once. Everyone laughed, even Rit.

Fortunately, Master Edward's new plantation was only ten miles away, so Ben was still able to visit his family. Ben and Rit managed to keep their marriage together, and their family kept on growing. Alongside three older sisters and a brother, Harriet had three more little brothers and another little sister by the time she was ten years old.

At night on the Brodess plantation, to keep her younger children amused, Rit would tell them stories in the cabin they shared.

'Let me tell you about Africa, the land where your grandmother was born,' she would always begin. 'Your grandmother's name was Modesty. But that wasn't her real name...'

Rit would repeat the stories that her own mother had told her many years ago. Tales about freedom in a strange and beautiful land, somewhere far across the ocean.

Lying awake on her bed of straw, Harriet tried to imagine what being free was like. It was hard to picture, as it was something she had never known. But she was sure of one thing – she wanted it for herself, more than anything else in the world.

3

Young Harriet: 1827

'Quick, Minty, Master Edward wants you!'

Linah leant against the doorpost of the cabin, gasping for breath. She had run all the way from the fields, where she was helping to gather the tobacco harvest in the blazing August heat.

Harriet laid her baby sister Rachel down in a wooden crate. The baby whimpered a little, but settled down into a light sleep. Aged just five years old, Harriet was in charge of looking after her two youngest siblings while her mother worked long hours in the kitchen up at the big house. Harriet crouched next to her little brother.

'Ben, I want you to watch baby Rachel for me,' she said, looking him in the eye. 'Stay here and don't try to follow me. Listen to me now: I need you to do as I say.'

Ben stared at her, his big brown eyes almost popping out of his head.

'Don't go, Minty!' he began, but Harriet cut him off.

'You're a good boy, Ben,' she said. 'I'll be back, don't worry.'

Linah walked with Harriet as far as the porch steps of the big house. She laid her hand on her little sister's shoulder.

'Master Edward's got plans for you,' she whispered. 'You may not be back for a while. I'll go and tell Ma.'

Harriet knew what this meant. Master Edward had decided it was time for her to start earning a living.

'Is he hiring me out?' she asked Linah.

Her sister nodded.

'Miss Susan came by asking for a nursemaid for her baby,' Linah said. Miss Susan was the wife of a slaveholder on a nearby plantation. 'So Master Edward jumped at the chance to send you. One less mouth to feed, and some more cash to help him pay off his debts.'

Everyone in the neighbourhood knew that Edward Brodess lived far beyond his means. When a plantation owner owed money, it was always bad news for his slaves. They could be hired out or sold at the drop of a hat. Linah hugged her little sister.

'It's your time now,' she said gently. 'Hold your chin up, and don't get yourself into trouble.'

With that, Linah ran off to tell Rit, and Harriet walked up to the wooden steps to the porch at the front of the big house. Miss Susan was standing there talking to Master Edward. She was so tall and thin in her grey silk dress, that Harriet could not imagine how she had ever produced a baby.

'Is this the one you mean?' asked Miss Susan, looking at Harriet with an expression of distain. 'Isn't she a bit small?' Harriet was tiny for her age, and looked even younger than her mere five years. Master Edward laughed uneasily.

'She's got a good head on her shoulders,' he said. 'You can rely on young Minty.'

He led Harriet towards the horse and carriage that was waiting on the drive. She turned around, looking frantically for her mother.

'Minty!' Rit cried, running down the porch steps after Harriet. She was still wearing her apron, and shaking flour from her hands.

'There's no time for goodbyes,' tutted Miss

Susan, pushing Harriet roughly into the carriage. Rit watched helplessly as her young daughter was driven away. Tears filled her eyes as the carriage turned the corner out of the drive and was gone.

* * *

Harriet took an instant dislike to Miss Susan, and the feeling appeared to be mutual. Try as she might, Harriet found it impossible to do anything right for her new mistress, and was given a beating for the smallest mistake. Miss Susan demanded Harriet stay up all night, to stop the baby from waking her when it cried. Whenever Harriet dozed off and the baby started wailing, Miss Susan would punish her severely.

'Will you never learn, child?' she would cry, grabbing hold of Harriet to whip her. 'Let this be a lesson to you.'

One morning, after a particularly bad night, Harriet was whipped five times before breakfast. The whip cut into her flesh so deeply that she carried the scars for the rest of her life. From that time on, Harriet did what she could to protect herself. Where possible, she put on extra layers of clothing, so that the thick material would help to protect her from beatings. She also screamed loudly whenever she was punished, so Miss Susan would think she was badly hurt. Later on in the day, when Harriet was out of Miss Susan's sight and less at risk of being beaten, she would take off her added padding.

Sometimes, Edward Brodess would hire Harriet out to work at other local plantations. Wherever she went, she was treated badly. That winter, Harriet was working for a planter called James Cook when she caught the measles. Cook refused to let her rest, but insisted she carry on working, despite her illness. Harriet was sent out in freezing rain to check muskrat traps on the riverbank. The river had risen so high, she had to wade up to her waist through the icy water to reach the traps. After completing her task, she staggered back to the house, and promptly collapsed with a fever. Harriet became so ill that Cook had to return her to the Brodess plantation.

Rit was shocked to see the state that Harriet was in after her short stint at the Cook plantation. She had no medicine to give her daughter, but she used river plants to make her own cures.

'Take this, Minty,' she said as she lifted Harriet's head so she could sip the bitter mixture from a cup. 'One day, when you're better, I'll show you how to make this potion, so you can help folk when they're sick.' Harriet was so weak she nearly died, but with painstaking care, Rit slowly nursed her back to health.

As soon as Harriet was well enough, Brodess sent her out to work again. A year later, aged only seven years old, she found herself back at Miss Susan's house. Miss Susan had a violent temper which she usually took out on her slaves, however one day, Harriet was working in the kitchen when Miss Susan picked a fight with her husband. Realizing that nobody was watching her, Harriet was gripped by a strong temptation. The sugar bowl was sitting just in front of her on the kitchen table, and she hadn't tasted anything sweet for such a long time...

Before she had time to think better of it, Harriet had picked up the largest sugar lump and popped it into her mouth. The taste was so divine it made her grin. Forgetting where she was for a moment, she stepped backwards and knocked over a stool.

The sudden clatter distracted Miss Susan from a long tirade against her husband. She turned to stare at Harriet.

'What in heaven's name...' she began angrily.

Guilt was written all over Harriet's face. Without thinking, she ran as fast as she could, dodging past Miss Susan and racing out through the kitchen door.

Wild ideas of escape formed in Harriet's mind. *I can't go back now*, she said to herself. *She whips me 'till I'm bloodied and bruised when I've done nothing wrong, so Lord help me now...*

Harriet ran out of the kitchen garden and down a muddy road. *I can't run back to Ma*, she thought, her mind racing as fast as her feet. *That would be the first place they'd look.*

She ran past a farmhouse and came to a pig sty, where an enormous sow was feeding her piglets. Harriet stopped in her tracks: this was the perfect hiding place.

Miss Susan treats me like an animal, she thought, *so why don't I just behave like one?* Glancing round to check that no one was looking, Harriet climbed over the wall and into the sty. The smell of dung was overpowering, but Harriet braced herself – she would just have to get used to it. She crawled inside the shelter and curled up on a bale of straw. Overcome with exhaustion, she quickly fell fast asleep.

When Harriet awoke, it was pitch dark. She must have been sleeping for hours. Feeling hungry, she went over to the feeding trough and nibbled on a few vegetable peelings.

I'll have to eat with the pigs until I can think of a better plan, she told herself.

The night passed, then another day and another night. Harriet was too frightened to run any further, and besides, she had nowhere else to go. After five days of living in the stinking muck with the pigs, she was faint with hunger.

I'd better give myself up if I want to survive, she resolved. Punishment, however brutal, would be better than a slow death from starvation. Harriet had experienced liberty of a sort, but now there would be a steep price to pay for it.

Harriet forced herself to trudge back to Miss Susan's house for the inevitable whipping. This time, there were no extra layers of clothing to soften the blows.

Wincing with pain, Harriet remembered her mother's words. 'They can hurt your body,' Rit had often told her, 'but they can never break your spirit.'

After this first bid for freedom, Harriet had reached a turning point in her young life. She knew what she wanted, and she was prepared to risk anything to get it. One day she would be free.

4

Sold South: 1830

'I can't see how we can help it,' Edward Brodess said to his wife Eliza one evening. They were sitting in front of a crackling fire, in the cosy sitting room of their plantation home. Their small children were asleep in bed upstairs.

'Help what, dear?' asked Eliza, peering at a tricky piece of needlework she was trying to finish.

'I haven't wanted to burden you with this, dearest,' he replied. 'But the fact is, we are short of money. We don't get nearly enough from hiring out our slaves – in fact some of them cause me nothing but trouble. Take young Minty, for example.'

Eliza chuckled. There was something about Harriet that made her smile.

'The time has come to sell off some of the family property to pay our debts,' Brodess went on.

'When I was at the market today, I met a trader from the Deep South, who offered me a fair price for Rit's oldest girls: Linah, Maria Ritty and Soph.'

The year was 1830, and Harriet was about eight. Her older sisters were all in their late teens and early twenties, and Linah now had small children of her own. About twenty years before, in 1808, a law had been passed banning ships from bringing slaves from Africa to sell in America. Now, the only legal way to buy and sell slaves was within America itself.

The slave market in America was a gold mine, and Brodess wanted to cash in on it. Everyone knew that life in the South was much harder for slaves than in the North; many slaves did not survive long in the harsh conditions of the southern cotton and rice plantations. But Brodess was too preoccupied with his own money worries to care much about the fate of his slaves.

'I can use the trader's payment to sort out my affairs,' he said to Eliza. 'I've got to look to the future for our family.' Eliza sighed. It was no use arguing with her husband once he had made up his mind, but she didn't feel happy about his decision.

'What about Rit?' she asked. 'She nursed you as a baby. You can't thank her for a lifetime of service by selling her family down south.' Brodess frowned and shook his head.

'We need this money,' he said firmly. 'Rit can't complain – she was lucky to keep her girls with her for so long.'

'But what about Linah's little ones?' asked Eliza. Linah had a toddler called Kessiah and a baby called Harriet. Eliza's children were the same age and she could not imagine the heartbreak of being parted from them.

'The trader isn't interested in babies,' said Brodess, dismissively. 'They'll just have to stay here. Minty can look after them – it will keep her out of trouble.'

The following day was one that young Harriet would never forget. The southern trader arrived on horseback with his men, and amidst scenes of great despair, took her big sisters away. Deep in her heart, Harriet knew she would never see her sisters again. Little Kessiah and the baby were too young to understand what was happening to their mother and aunts. The three young women screamed as they were dragged off the plantation; Linah wailing for her babies as if her heart was being torn in two. The agony on their faces was something that would haunt Harriet until her dying day.

For hours after they had gone, Rit could not be moved from her vantage point by the plantation gate. She had been standing there as she watched her daughters disappear from sight down the road. Now she was rooted to the spot, a statue of untouchable grief. For once, Ben didn't even try to console her. Overcome by his own private pain, he staggered back to the cabin, leaning on young Harriet for support. She was their oldest daughter now.

'They're lost to us,' he said to Harriet. 'May God be with them. You'll have to watch out for your Ma and Pa from now on, Minty...' With that, Ben broke down. Harriet had never seen her father cry before.

That night, for the first time in her life, Harriet had a terrible nightmare. She woke up in a sweat, still hearing the pounding hooves of horsemen coming to take her away to a kind of slavery worse than anything she had ever known. For many years afterwards, her sleep was broken by this recurrent and harrowing night vision.

There was nothing Ben and Rit could do to reunite their broken family. But as Rit slowly came back to her senses, a steely resolve settled on her and she vowed she would never let such a tragedy happen again.

'I'll die before I lose another child of mine,' she swore.

Four years later, Rit's worst fears were put to the test. One morning, when Harriet was about twelve years old, Miss Eliza sent her on an errand to the goods store in Bucktown, near the Brodess plantation. Just outside the store, Harriet met a slave boy on the run. He was about her age.

'My master's inside that store,' whispered the boy. He looked terrified. 'Please don't let him catch me.' Harriet pictured herself as a small child, frightened and alone in a stinking pig sty. Her biggest fear had been that her mistress would find her and beat her to kingdom come. She knew she had to help her fellow slave.

'I'll make a diversion,' Harriet told the boy, thinking fast. 'Then you'll be able to get away.'

But at that moment, someone walked out of the store and the boy's master spotted the runaway through the open doorway. His thin, red face twisted with anger.

'Stop that boy!' the master shouted at Harriet, but she stood still, refusing to obey his order. The man grabbed an iron weight from some measuring scales on the shop counter and hurled it at his wayward slave. Fortunately for the boy, his master's aim was terrible. The weight struck Harriet instead, catching her just above her left eye and smashing into her skull with a sickening crunch. The puffy white clouds swirled around in the blue sky above Harriet's head. She fell backwards, and everything went dark.

With blood pouring from her wound, Harriet was carried back to the Brodess plantation. She was unconscious, and seriously hurt. Rit laid her daughter out on a table and refused to leave her side.

'Minty needs a doctor!' she pleaded with Master Edward, but her request fell on deaf ears. Doctors were far too expensive to be wasted on slaves, and troublesome ones at that. But Miss Eliza took pity on Harriet's mother.

'You can tend to her yourself, Rit,' she said. 'Just mind you don't slack off on your work around the house.'

The accident nearly killed Harriet, but for months, Rit nursed her daughter until her strength returned. Meanwhile, Edward Brodess tried his best to sell his accident-prone young slave. Sick and injured, Harriet was of no use to him any more; but no one was interested in buying her, even at a rock bottom price.

'It's a miracle you're still with us,' Rit said to Harriet one day. 'God must have sent his angels to protect you.' As always, Harriet wasn't interested in herself.

'Ma, tell me the truth, now,' she said. 'What happened to that poor boy at Bucktown Stores?'

'I don't know, Minty,' Rit replied, shaking her head. 'I hope he got away in all that mayhem you caused.'

Harriet smiled. 'I pray to God he did,' she said.

As well as leaving a physical scar, Harriet's brain injury caused her to suffer regular blackouts and bouts of illness. Like all her family, Harriet was a devout Christian, but her accident seemed to make her even more religious than before. She began to have visions, which she believed were communications from God.

'I know God will always keep me safe,' she would say to her brothers and sister. 'He tells me so in my dreams. And I know he'll take care of you, too.'

Harriet's strange blackouts made it hard for her to work in the big house at the Brodess plantation. At a loss to know what to do with his awkward young slave, Edward Brodess sent Harriet out to labour in the fields. Despite her recent injury, she soon became strong and resilient. When Harriet was thirteen years old, Brodess finally managed to find her long-term employment.

'That Minty's a funny one,' Brodess said to his wife Eliza. 'She's as strong as an ox, despite everything that's happened to her. I'm going to hire her out to a merchant and shipbuilder on the Eastern Shore, who goes by the name of John Stewart. He's promised to pay good money for her.'

Harriet was happy with this arrangement. She went to work in an area called Tobacco Stick, not far from where she was born, and near where her father Ben still lived. For his part, Ben was happy to have his daughter close by him at last. He was an expert timber inspector, relied upon to manage the forests on his master's land. But he also had a secret life, which he was keen to share with Harriet.

'I'm proud of what you did for that runaway in Bucktown,' Ben said to Harriet one night. They were toasting pork over a fire outside Ben's forest cabin. 'You know, Minty, for years I've been helping fugitive slaves myself. They pass through these parts on their journey north to the free states. I tell them the lie of the land and help them on their way.'

'Where do they go?' asked Harriet, chewing thoughtfully on a hot piece of meat.

'Most folk end up in New York State or Pennsylvania, some carry on across the border to Canada,' her father replied. 'They go wherever slavery's against the law.'

'Do they make it?' Harriet asked.

'Some do, some don't,' Ben replied. 'But they all figure it's a risk they have to take.'

Harriet had heard nasty rumours of murders and brutal mutilations carried out by slave catchers. Escaping from slavery was a dangerous business. She thought hard for a moment, and felt the scar on her left temple throb a little.

'I agree with your fugitives, Pa,' she said, slowly. 'Freedom is a prize worth fighting for. I'm beginning to think I won't rest until I've tasted it for myself.'

Harriet leant forward to poke a stick at the bonfire. A spark flew upwards, glowing in the dark.

'We should all be free,' she said. 'This slavery is the next thing to hell.'

5

False Start: 1844

Edward Brodess threw back his head and laughed out loud.

'Do you know what you're taking on?' he said. 'That Minty's as stubborn as a mule!'

John Tubman stood up to his full height and looked Harriet's master in the eye.

'I'll thank you not to speak about my future wife in that way,' he replied. Immediately he regretted his words.

I've gone too far, he thought.

'Forgive me, sir,' he said hastily. 'I would like your permission to marry Minty.'

Even though John Tubman was a free black, he had to be careful not to upset any white man, or there could be serious consequences. The law did not treat free blacks the same as white

43

Americans. Former slaves had very few rights, and were routinely discriminated against by the courts, particularly in disputes with white people. Fortunately for John Tubman, Brodess decided not to take offence at his rash words.

'Why, you're welcome to the girl,' he replied. 'She'll still belong to me, whatever you both choose to do.'

John Tubman heaved a sigh of relief. He was keen to marry Harriet, whom he had met while working on the Brodess plantation. He was about 32, ten years older than Harriet, and was a good-looking man of mixed race. He was captivated by Harriet's lively determination and feisty character. In turn, Harriet had fallen for John's carefree, easy manner, which seemed a natural consequence of his precious freedom.

Unlike the fugitive slaves that Harriet's father helped on their way north, John had not been forced to escape to win his freedom. He was a free man because his mother had been given her liberty many years ago. Like John's mother, Harriet's father was no longer a slave. He had been granted his freedom after the death of his master Anthony Thompson, four years before. But Harriet was still owned by Edward Brodess and remained his property.

For Harriet, the biggest obstacle to marriage was her status as a slave.

'I do want to be your wife, John...' she said to him that night, as the couple walked together through the woods. The moonlight was casting a tangle of shadows on the ground. There was an uncomfortable pause.

'So what is the problem, then?' asked John. 'Brodess has given us permission.'

'You know how I feel,' replied Harriet sadly. 'I'm a slave, and you are not. Our children will be born into slavery. They will belong to Master Edward, who could decide to sell them, or me, at any time.'

John was naturally optimistic, but even he had to admit this was a dismal vision of the future.

'I've seen it all before,' Harriet continued, shaking her head. 'Losing poor Linah, Maria Ritty and Soph broke my mother's heart.'

'It will be different for us, Minty, I promise,' said John. 'We can buy your freedom – we can save for it! Then our children will be born free.'

It was an intoxicating thought. Harriet smiled, and gave her fiancé a kiss.

'You win, as usual,' she said. 'Let's do it. Let's get married.'

A few weeks later, the wedding took place on the Brodess plantation.

'I'm not a child any more,' Harriet told her parents, as they embraced their newly-wed daughter. 'From now on, I don't want you to call me Minty.' She turned to all her friends and family at the informal wedding party.

'You can call me Harriet, after my dear mother, and I'll also take my husband's name,' she announced. 'Minty Ross has grown up – I'm Harriet Tubman now.'

* * *

Five years passed. In all that time, Harriet did not fall pregnant, and the couple's cabin remained quiet and empty. John was not happy about the situation.

'How can we bring a child into the world who does not even belong to us?' Harriet argued, again and again. It was proving almost impossible to save enough money to buy Harriet's precious freedom.

Cracks began to form in the marriage. Both Harriet and John worked long hours and saw very little of each other. Harriet continued working for a timber gang, driving oxen and hauling wood, despite suffering from frequent blackouts caused by her old head injury.

'Your daughter's worth at least two strong men,' one of Harriet's friends joked to her father, Ben. 'She may be only five feet tall, but she's mighty tough!'

One night in February 1849, at the end of a long day's work in the freezing forest, Ben noticed that Harriet looked unhappy.

'What's up?' he asked. Harriet shrugged. She was thinking about returning home to yet another argument with John.

'Why don't you come back to my cabin tonight?' asked her father, as if reading her mind. 'I'd like you to meet some good friends of mine.'

That evening, Ben introduced Harriet to his secret circle of slaves and freemen. They talked late into the night, sharing information about escape plans, and possible routes to freedom in the North.

Feeling frustrated and trapped by her life, Harriet found the discussion very exciting.

If only I could run away too, she thought.

A week later, Rit had some bad news for Harriet when she came to visit.

'It's Master Edward,' Rit said. 'He's done some terrible things over the years, but...' She paused to wipe her eyes, and Harriet saw that her hands were shaking.

'Is he sick, Ma?' Harriet asked. Rit nodded.

'The doctor up at the big house says he's only got a few days to live.'

Harriet knew exactly what this meant. For years, their master's debts had been common knowledge. There was no chance of Edward Brodess granting them freedom in his will. When he died, his widow Eliza would have to pay the bills, and she would do it in the only way she knew how: she would sell her slaves to the highest bidder.

On March 7th 1849, Brodess died at the age of forty-seven. Eliza lost no time in tackling her inherited debts; within weeks, she put the daughters of Harriet's older sister Linah up for sale. By now, Kessiah and her sister were grown up, with small children of their own. Harriet could not stop this auction, but she refused to stay around to be sold herself. There was only one possible course of action.

Harriet prayed her husband would understand.

'Escape with me!' she pleaded, when they talked the situation over. 'We can start a new life in the North. We will have children, I promise, and they will all be free!' But deep down, Harriet knew that John would never agree to run away with her.

'You are asking me to take a huge risk,' he told Harriet. For once he did not get angry, but he sat still on their bed, holding his head in his hands. 'You may have made up your mind, but it is not so easy for me. Remember, I am a free man. If I'm caught helping you to escape, I'll be made a slave again.'

Tears streamed down Harriet's face. She knew John was speaking the truth.

'I'm sorry, Harriet. I can't do it,' he said, his voice cracking. 'I can't go back to a life of slavery.'

Harriet could stay with her husband, which meant taking the risk of being sold south, or she could try to escape to freedom, leaving her marriage and family behind.

It was a painful choice, but it was one she had already made. 'Forgive me, John,' she said, brushing away her tears. 'But we both know what I'm going to do.'

The decision now made, Harriet was more determined to escape than ever, but felt unsure about making such a bold move all alone. She was familiar with the local terrain, having worked all her life on the forests and waterways of Dorchester County. But even so, she felt vulnerable setting off by herself.

Two of Harriet's younger brothers worked with her on the Thompson plantation – Ben, who was now twenty-five and Henry, still just nineteen years old. Both of them were inspired by Harriet's ambition to escape.

'We'll come with you,' said Henry, with youthful enthusiasm.

Ben was more cautious, as he had a young family. But he too, dreamed of making a free life for himself in the North, then returning to rescue his wife and children.

'We can do this,' he said to Harriet. 'You've got enough determination for all of us!'

On the night of the 17th September 1849, Harriet began her journey with Ben and Henry. To start with, luck was on their side. Due to a lack of communication between the Thompson and Brodess plantations, Eliza Brodess did not realize her slaves were missing for at least a week. However on discovering that three of her valuable assets had run away, an outraged Eliza immediately placed an advertisement in the county newspaper, offering a handsome reward for their capture.

As soon as Ben saw the advertisement, his spirits sank. He showed it to Harriet and Henry.

'We're done for,' he said. They were hiding in a barn waiting for the sun to set, before they could continue on their way that night. 'The slave catchers will get us now.'

Both Ben and Henry lost their nerve; they were terrified at the prospect of being caught and brutally punished.

'I can't go through with this,' Ben said to Harriet. 'I want to see my wife and children again in this life, not the next.'

When darkness fell, Ben and Henry began the trek home, taking Harriet with them against her better judgement. They handed themselves in to Eliza Brodess, hoping to avoid serious punishment. Ben tried to convince Harriet, and himself, that they had done the right thing.

'The chances are, we'll only be sold round these parts,' he said, desperately. 'We won't need to leave everyone behind.'

Back in her cabin at Peters Neck, Harriet was reunited with her husband. She felt angry and ashamed at the failure of her plans.

'I hope this little adventure chased all those escape plans out of your head,' John teased. But the setback had only strengthened Harriet's resolve.

'No, John,' she said, looking into his eyes. 'Next time, I'll just have to go it alone.'

6

North Star: 1849

The time had finally come and Harriet was as prepared as she would ever be. She checked her small bag of provisions once more, and looked over towards her husband John, to check that he was still sleeping. He was snoring softly, and as an owl hooted outside, he stirred, turning his back to Harriet.

Goodbye John, Harriet thought. *Forgive me for leaving you like this.*

After Harriet's failed attempt to escape three weeks earlier, the couple had barely spoken to one another. To prevent further rows, Harriet had kept her new escape plans a secret from her husband. And tonight, the last thing she wanted was a noisy argument to jeopardize her chances of success.

Harriet's father Ben had been a great comfort to her since her return, as well as a huge practical help as she considered running away for a second time.

'If you are serious about this, Harriet, you can't do it all by yourself,' he had told her. 'You've got to ask for help from the Underground Railroad.' This was the name given to the secret network of people, black, white, enslaved and free, who were dedicated to helping slaves escape to freedom in the North.

Harriet nodded.

'I know a wise old lady, a Quaker, who has organised many escapes,' Ben went on. 'She is a good Christian woman who believes slavery is a sin. You must go and see her.'

The next night, Harriet had visited the old woman, a 'stationmaster' on the Underground Railroad who sheltered runaway slaves on their journey to freedom.

'I have written down the names of people who will take you in, and the places where they live,' the woman had told Harriet, giving her a folded piece of paper. Harriet grimaced; she couldn't read, so how could this possibly help her? The woman smiled kindly at Harriet's worried expression.

'You must show this to the stationmasters along the way, so they know I have sent you,' she said gently. 'I will tell you what it says, so you can remember the details.'

Harriet felt incredibly moved by the danger this woman was prepared to face on her behalf. If she was caught helping a fugitive, she could be sentenced to lengthy imprisonment, or worse.

But now, it was time for Harriet to begin her real journey. The moonless sky was pitch black, and a scattering of bright stars sparkled overhead. Harriet looked for one star in particular; a star which her father had taught her to find.

'Follow the North Star,' Ben had told her. 'That way, you'll always be heading in the right direction.' Remembering her father's words, Harriet set out on her way.

As Harriet crept through the dense gum tree forest, sharp stones and seed pods stabbed at the soles of her feet. Just before leaving, she had followed her father's advice and rubbed her feet with the foul-smelling resin from the asafetida plant.

'That will put off the dogs that come after you,' Ben had told her. He knew his daughter was terrified of the bloodhounds that the slave catchers used to hunt down fugitive slaves.

Please God, don't let them begin the chase tonight, she prayed. *Help me to get a head start!*

Harriet's prayers were answered. By the next morning, she reached the first safe house on her route. Harriet showed her handwritten note to the white woman waiting by the door.

'Welcome,' the woman said, smiling at Harriet. 'Come in and rest. But later I'll give you some work to do, so it will look like you're supposed to be here.'

After a few hours of desperately needed sleep, Harriet set to work sweeping the yard.

'Look busy,' the woman said. 'That way, no one will guess you're on the run.'

That evening, the woman's husband returned from working in the fields. Under cover of darkness, he loaded up his wagon, hiding Harriet under some blankets.

'I'll drive you on from here,' he said to Harriet. 'The weather is set fair tonight, so we should make good progress.'

The next day, Harriet rested, then at nightfall she continued on her way. She kept up this nocturnal pattern for her whole journey, covering most of the ninety miles to the Pennsylvanian state border on foot. Some days, Harriet found a place to rest in the forest. The best hiding places were usually hollowed out tree trunks, near colonies of brown bats that snapped up the pesky mosquitoes. Whenever Harriet could, she sheltered by day in safe houses, and somehow, she avoided the slave catchers who were hell-bent on hunting her down.

One bright morning in late October, Harriet finally reached her destination. The sun was rising and a new day was dawning. As she crossed over the border into the state of Pennsylvania, Harriet became a free woman at last. Taking a deep breath, Harriet looked down at her hands – they were the same as they had always been, but inside, everything was transformed. A shaft of autumn sunlight shone through the flame-coloured leaves on the trees, and the harvest stubble in the fields seemed to glow with a golden haze. Harriet pinched herself, to check she was not having another one of her vivid dreams.

I must be in heaven, she thought.

* * *

'Harriet, there's a boy here with an urgent message for you!' said one of the waiters at the busy hotel kitchen. Harriet looked up from her sink full of dirty pots and pans.

'Thank you,' she said, wiping her soapy hands on a towel. She had been working at this hotel in Philadelphia for a few weeks now, one of the many casual jobs she had found since arriving in the city a year ago.

After the initial euphoria of freedom, the reality of Harriet's new life had sunk in. Philadelphia was an exciting place to live, but things were not easy for the constant stream of runaway slaves arriving in the city. Jobs were exhausting and badly paid, and prejudice against black people was common, and often violent. There was also the constant threat of kidnap by ruthless slave dealers, who sold their unlucky victims back into slavery in the Deep South. With growing dismay, Harriet realized she had embraced a very fragile kind of freedom.

Worst of all, Harriet was lonely. She desperately missed her family and friends back in Maryland. The community of runaways in Philadelphia was close-knit, and any news from the slave states was quickly shared on the local grapevine. As Harriet ran out of the hotel kitchen to find the message boy, her heart was thumping fast in her chest.

Will it be bad news? she wondered. *Has anybody died?*

The boy was waiting at the tradesman's entrance to the hotel.

'I have a message from a free black man called John Bowley,' he began.

That's Kessiah's husband, thought Harriet.

'Please go on,' she said.

'John Bowley's wife is about to be sold with her two children,' said the boy. 'She is in Cambridge now, on the eastern side of Chesapeake Bay. John needs your help to rescue her – he's waiting to meet you in Baltimore, on the western side of the bay.'

There was no question in Harriet's mind. She would leave immediately. She had always been planning to return to rescue her family, and had saved everything she had earned over the last year to help pay for her first trip. She handed the message boy a generous tip.

'Thank you for your trouble,' she said.

Harriet was fully aware of the danger she was

putting herself in. She could easily be captured, re-enslaved, or deliberately crippled, so that she couldn't escape again. She knew of some unfortunate slaves whose heels had been slashed for this very reason. But Harriet was prepared to take this risk, for the ultimate prize of bringing her family to freedom.

Once in Baltimore, Harriet went into hiding with some family friends before meeting up with John Bowley. Together, the pair worked out a plan of action to rescue Kessiah and the children. It would be incredibly risky, but with the auction fast approaching, it was the only chance they had.

'God be with you,' Harriet said to Bowley the next day, as he boarded a boat bound for the port of Cambridge. Now all she could do was wait.

On the day of the auction, Bowley wore a disguise and stood in the crowds at the Cambridge Court House. When the bidding began, he made the highest offer for his wife and children, securing the sale. During the midday break, Bowley pretended to go off to make arrangements to pay, but in reality sneaked back into the court house. Once inside, he smuggled Kessiah and the children to a safe house, located just five minutes' walk away. When the auctioneer returned from his dinner and discovered his valuable property had disappeared, he was furious. He immediately ordered a search, but the missing slaves were nowhere to be found.

Late that night, John Bowley stowed his family away in a small wooden boat in the harbour.

'Where are we going, Papa?' asked his daughter.

'To see your Aunt Harriet,' he replied. 'We need to sail across the bay to Baltimore tonight.'

'But it's so windy!' cried his young son. 'Will we be safe?'

Kessiah shot a tense glance at her husband.

'It will be safer than staying here, my darling,' she said. 'Sixty miles is nothing if we've got a good wind behind us.'

After a stormy night on the water, Bowley and his family finally reached Baltimore, where Harriet was waiting for them. Kessiah clambered out of the boat and ran to greet her aunt. She was soaked to the skin from the wind and rain.

'Now you're here, Harriet, I know we're safe!' she cried, bursting into tears.

'Almost, Kizzy,' Harriet said. 'But we still have

some way to go.' Using all her skills of nocturnal navigation, Harriet safely brought her relatives back to Philadelphia, to live with her there.

Harriet was encouraged by the success of her first rescue, but also deeply unsettled by it. More and more often she thought of her parents, her siblings and especially her husband, John, whom she had abandoned in the night so many months before.

'I must leave you for a while,' she said to Kessiah one day. 'I want to bring my husband here, so we can live together in freedom, just like you and your family.'

Working tirelessly, Harriet had managed to save enough money to buy her husband a suit of clothes for the return journey. Finally she set off, retracing the steps of her escape route two years earlier.

After a tiring and difficult journey, Harriet eventually arrived at her old neighbourhood. It was too risky for her to let her parents know she was back; the fewer people she saw, the safer they would all be. Harriet took shelter with some Underground Railroad friends instead. They greeted her arrival with bad news.

'We're so sorry, Harriet,' they said, exchanging worried looks.

Harriet feared the worst. 'Has my husband died?' she cried.

'No, no, he is alive and well,' came the hushed reply. 'But he has taken another wife, a free woman called Caroline.'

Harriet could not take it in. She picked up the sack of clothes she had carried so many miles for her husband. It felt like a dead weight.

'Tell him that I'm here,' she said, and sat down.

A few hours later, Harriet's friends returned, but John was not with them. Harriet sighed; if John could not bring himself to face her, then he wasn't worth her breath, let alone a fight. There was no point in rushing over to the cabin they had once shared, to make a scene in front of his new wife.

'If he can do without me, then I can do without him,' she said simply.

Determined that all the effort she had made to return would not go to waste, Harriet gathered together a group of eleven slaves to travel back with her to Philadelphia. For Harriet, freedom for her people was more important than an unfaithful husband. There were far more urgent matters to worry about.

7

Family Matters: 1854

It was December 1854, and Harriet was about to spend Christmas with Kessiah and her family. They were living in Canada now, because a new law, the 'Bloodhound Act', made it unsafe for ex-slaves to live in the northern states of America. By law, all Americans were now forced to hand over runaway slaves to their owners, even in states like Pennsylvania, where slavery had been abolished years ago.

The streets of St Catharines were thick with snow. The quiet town where Harriet had settled was on the Canadian side of the Niagara Falls, in the state of Ontario. Harriet was walking home to the small house that she shared with Kessiah and her family. She had spent the day with some new arrivals from America. Like many runaway slaves, these people were having problems adjusting to their newfound freedom, and Harriet had been helping them find food, clothing and shelter.

I need a rest, thought Harriet, as she reached the front door. *I can't wait for the Christmas holidays!*

It had been a busy couple of years since Harriet had returned from Maryland with eleven rescued slaves in tow. Inspired by the success of this mass escape, she had since set out on several more rescue missions to guide grateful groups of fugitives to freedom in the North.

Kessiah opened the door to Harriet.

'Come in and sit down,' she said. 'You've been so busy with all your good works and daring trips down south, we've hardly seen you!' Harriet smiled wearily and took a seat by the fire to warm her hands.

'The children want to have you all to themselves this Christmas,' Kessiah said, bustling around the small kitchen. 'And I don't want you to lift a finger!'

'That sounds wonderful, Kizzy,' Harriet replied. But her thoughts lay elsewhere. She had heard on the grapevine that things were not going well for her brothers Robert, Ben and Henry back in

Dorchester County, and she couldn't stop worrying about them.

At that moment, John, Kessiah's husband burst in through the door. He was out of breath from running, and in too much of a rush to stamp the snow from his feet.

'Harriet, have you heard the news?' he asked. 'I've just been told Miss Eliza is planning to sell your brothers over the Christmas holidays. I reckon she must need to lay her hands on some quick cash.'

Harriet sighed. She had feared as much. There was nothing for it; she would have to make another journey south – and without delay.

'I'm sorry, Kizzy,' she said, leaping out of her chair. 'It looks like the children may have to wait a little longer for my company.'

Harriet thought long and hard about the best way to conduct this escape mission. It would be more dangerous than usual, because it would take her right into the heart of the community where she was most well known. One false step, and it could be her last. She decided to send word to her brothers first, to warn them that she was on her way.

The next morning, she took the first steam train across the border, heading south for Philadelphia. She went to visit an old friend of hers, a free black man who could read and write. Like most former slaves, Harriet had never been taught these basic skills.

'Can you write a letter for me?' Harriet asked her friend. 'I'll dictate it to you, to send to an Underground Railroad contact of mine who lives near my brothers in Maryland. He'll make sure they get the message.'

As with many of Harriet's secret communications, her letter was worded in coded, biblical language. In it, she told Robert, Ben and Henry to 'step aboard when the good ship of Zion comes along'. She knew that as soon as her brothers heard this instruction, they would know their sister was coming to get them.

Back on the Brodess plantation, Robert, Ben and Henry did not tell a soul about Harriet's letter. Henry could not even tell his wife, who was about to have her third baby. He knew if he didn't take this opportunity to escape, he would be sold to the Deep South and parted from his family forever. Unlike his failed escape bid five years earlier, Henry knew that this time, there could be no turning back.

Harriet's brothers worked out a plan of action.

'We need to get Miss Eliza's permission to visit our parents on Christmas Day,' said Robert, the oldest of the three brothers.

'That should be easy,' said Henry, the youngest. 'Nothing suspicious there.'

'We won't arrive for Christmas dinner though,' said Ben. 'We'll hide in a barn nearby to wait for Harriet instead. It's perfect timing – no one will miss us at this time of year.'

Everything went smoothly and Harriet met up with her brothers as arranged. She felt it was too risky to let their mother in on the scheme – it had been five years since Rit had last seen Harriet, and Harriet knew she would find it too painful to let her leave again, especially if her sons were going too. But Harriet was happy to tell her father; she trusted his experience of helping fugitives. Ingenious as ever, Harriet thought of a way for Ben to meet them, without endangering their escape plan. Late on Christmas Day, Harriet arranged to have Ben brought to the barn where she and her brothers were hiding. He would be wearing a blindfold.

'Pa can swear on the Bible he hasn't seen us,' Harriet explained to her brothers as they waited for him. 'He's an honest Christian, so everyone will believe him, even Ma!'

When Ben appeared, Harriet ran to embrace him.

'We're so proud of you, Minty,' said Ben, his blindfold damp with tears. He pulled at the tightly wrapped cloth, as if to take it off, but Harriet stopped him.

'The blindfold's for your own good, Pa,' she reminded him, clasping his hands in her own.

In her cabin nearby, Rit was frantic; her sons had not arrived when she expected them to, many hours ago. She paced about the cabin nervously, drawing heavily on her wooden pipe. Just before midnight, Ben came in through the door.

'Have you seen our boys?' Rit cried.

'No, I haven't laid eyes on them,' he replied truthfully. 'But I figure they've followed the North Star, just like Harriet did, all those years ago.' Rit shook her head and sighed.

'If that's true, they're in the Lord's hands now,' she said.

Avoiding direct contact with her parents was one of the hardest things Harriet had ever had to do. But she could not allow her emotions to cloud her judgement. With cool determination, Harriet led the way north for her brothers. Along the way they stopped to rest at safe houses, known as 'stations' by the people who worked on the Underground Railroad. The 'stationmasters' provided them with food, water, shoes, clothes and the medical care they needed to survive. When comfortable shelters were hard to find, the forests, swamps, marshes and creeks of Maryland's Eastern Shore provided perfect cover for Harriet and her brothers.

Sometimes, Harriet left her brothers to sleep by day, while she scouted the local area for food and information. She used every trick in the book to hide her identity. Sometimes she wore disguises, either dressing as a respectable free man or a frail elderly woman.

'No one would guess how old I really am!' Harriet said, pointing her walking stick at her brothers.

'You still look like my baby sister to me,' laughed Robert. He was thirty-eight, and Harriet was thirty-two years old.

One day, when Harriet had to venture out along a busy street, she set off with some chickens under her arms.

'What are they for, Harriet?' asked Ben. He was Harriet's younger brother by two years, and had always asked her lots of questions, ever since he was a toddler. Harriet smiled.

'These chickens will be a lifesaver, Ben,' she replied. 'If I get into trouble and need a quick getaway, I'll let them loose to make a distraction.'

At last, sometime in the New Year of 1855, Harriet and her brothers made it safely across the border to freedom in Canada. Robert, Ben and Henry were glad to escape from slavery, but their emotions were mixed. Much of the journey had been spent worrying about their wives and children, and inspired by their sister's example, they resolved to go back and rescue their families as soon as possible.

The reunion with Kessiah and her family in St Catharines was bittersweet. The brothers' joy was tempered with a longing for those they had left behind. Harriet understood these reservations, but for herself, she felt she would burst with happiness.

'Seeing you together again is such a wonderful reward after all the hardship and danger we have faced on the road,' she said to Kessiah, blinking back tears.

* * *

When Harriet first began her trips on the Underground Railroad, she had to save her own wages to pay for her expeditions. But as the 1850s wore on, word spread of Harriet's success, and anti-slavery societies began to give her money to fund her daring missions. Most years, she would rescue a party of slaves in the autumn, returning to Canada to rest with her family during the winter. In spring and summer, she would give fund-raising talks in northern American cities, all the while preparing for her next autumn rescue.

By 1857, three years had passed since Harriet led her brothers to freedom. Harriet worried constantly about her parents, who were still in Dorchester County and now in their seventies. Even though Ben and Rit were no longer slaves, they were still in danger because of their involvement with the

Underground Railroad. One day, Harriet heard through the grapevine that her father was facing arrest for helping runaways.

I'm not surprised, thought Harriet. *It was only a matter of time before the law caught up with them. I've got to help them escape.*

So once again, Harriet crept back to the place of her birth. Ben and Rit were overjoyed to see their daughter again after so many years.

'I always knew you'd come,' said Rit, tearfully. 'But we're too old to walk far these days. How can we travel all that way with you?'

Harriet squeezed her mother's frail hand. 'I've thought of that, Ma,' she replied. 'You need to gather together all the rickety wagon parts you can find, and I'll build a makeshift cart for you.'

The night before they began their journey, Ben had a private talk with Harriet. He was well aware of the risks that lay ahead.

'Don't forget, even the forest has eyes,' he told Harriet, 'There are vigilantes everywhere.' But Ben had underestimated his daughter's skill in the art of undercover travel. Against all odds, the rescue was a success and Harriet finally managed to bring her parents to St Catharines, Canada, to be reunited with their family.

'I never thought I'd live to see this day!' sobbed Rit, as she kissed her children one by one. 'If only Rachel was here with us too...' Harriet's younger sister Rachel and her children were still back in Maryland on the Brodess plantation. Rit did not mention Linah, Maria Ritty and Soph, although she had never forgotten her long-lost daughters. She did not know if they were dead or alive, but she had come to accept that they would never meet again.

Harriet sensed her mother's anguish. She understood that even the joy of liberation could not stamp out the pain of separation and loss. She kissed Rit's hands and looked her straight in the eye.

'I'll go back for Rachel as soon as I can, Ma,' she said firmly. 'I'm not going to let them take my little sister away from me too.'

8

General Tubman: 1858

There was a sharp knock at the door of Harriet's house in St Catharines.

'Is this the residence of Mrs Tubman?' boomed a loud voice.

It was early afternoon, and the commotion woke old Ben and Rit, who had just dozed off for an afternoon nap.

'What's going on, Harriet?' Rit asked, as her daughter ran to answer the door.

'I don't know, Ma, but there must be some emergency. I hope it isn't anything to do with Rachel.'

In the year since Harriet had returned to Canada with her parents, she had already made one unsuccessful attempt to go back south for her younger sister. But she could not persuade Rachel to leave her two children behind in Maryland – they were working on different plantations and had been unable to sneak away to join the rescue party. As had happened before when Harriet returned for her errant husband, she had come back with a motley band of fugitives instead.

Harriet opened the door a crack.

'I'm Harriet Tubman,' she said. 'And who might you be, sir?'

An old white man with a shock of grey hair and a thick bushy beard was standing on the doorstep. He looked familiar.

'Have we met before?' Harriet asked, and the old man laughed.

'You may have seen my portrait – just like you, I'm a wanted person in some parts of America. I fight slavery whenever I can – it's my greatest passion!'

Of course… thought Harriet. *Why didn't I recognize him straight away?*

'John Brown!' she said, opening the door. 'Do come in, sir, it's an honour to meet you.'

John Brown was a hero for many people, black and white, who were fighting to get rid of slavery. Such people, considered 'radical' by many more conservative Americans, were known as abolitionists.

'The honour is all mine,' said John Brown, bowing. Harriet took a step back in utter shock – no white man had ever bowed to her before.

'I was at one of your speeches last week, when you told stories about your brave adventures on the Underground Railroad,' he said. 'It was a fine talk – I should think you raised a good sum of money for our cause.'

John Brown was at my talk! Harriet thought, with amazement. Her speeches at abolitionist meetings were becoming increasingly popular, and to some, she had even become known as 'Moses', after the Old Testament leader who led his people from slavery to freedom in the Promised Land. By now, Harriet had helped over seventy runaway slaves to escape.

At the speech, Harriet had described some of the tight scrapes she had experienced on her trips with the Underground Railroad. She entertained her audience with a tale of how she had avoided being recognized by hiding behind a newspaper, hoping her former master would only remember her as an illiterate slave. Fortunately, she had held the newspaper the right way up... She also explained why she always asked people to rip down 'wanted' posters, in order to improve a runaway's chances. This was because she had once fallen asleep underneath her own 'wanted' poster, offering a reward of twelve thousand dollars to anyone who would turn her in.

'That was a lucky escape!' she had joked.

John Brown was intrigued by one particular aspect of Harriet's speech.

'You said that you always take a gun with you,' he said. 'Why?'

'The one thing I can't risk is a member of my escape party panicking, or trying to turn round and go home,' Harriet replied. 'It only takes one person to lose their nerve for the safety of the whole group to be compromised. I take a gun, and I threaten to use it on any one who puts the whole group in danger. One dead runaway is a price I'd be prepared to pay to lead the rest of a group to safety.'

'Would you ever use your gun?' persisted John Brown, staring at her with his piercing blue eyes.

'Well, yes, I believe I would,' Harriet replied. 'But, thank the Lord, I haven't needed to yet.'

There was a pause.

'I need your help, General Tubman!' John Brown said at last. Harriet laughed, somewhat confused.

'I'm afraid you are mistaken, Mr Brown,' she said. 'I'm not a man, and I'm not in the army!'

John Brown sniffed dismissively.

'I'm serious,' he said. 'I have complete faith in your abilities. I'm here to recruit you for my latest campaign.'

The famous abolitionist went on to explain to Harriet his plans to mount an armed attack on a weapons store in a place called Harpers Ferry, in the American state of West Virginia. He wanted to free a large number of slaves in order to draw attention to the anti-slavery movement.

'Peaceful speeches are not enough,' he argued. 'We need to take up arms and fight for freedom.'

Harriet was surprised to find herself agreeing with this white man's enthusiasm for militant action. She had always thought of slavery as being a sin, but now, Brown was helping her to see it as an act of war.

'Help me to prepare for this raid on Harpers Ferry,' Brown said to Harriet. 'No one knows better than you how to organize a secret operation.' He knew just how to flatter her, and she could not resist his persuasive, if unconventional charms.

'Count me in, sir,' she said.

Harriet spent the next six months raising funds for John Brown's attack on Harpers Ferry. However, in October of the next year, when the raid on the weapons store finally took place, Harriet did not take part. For some time, she had sensed that Brown's plans were flawed, so with a heavy heart, she had decided not to travel south to join in the action. As she had feared, John Brown's bold scheme ended in failure, leading to his arrest and execution for treason. He was hanged on December 2nd 1859, becoming an instant martyr for his cause.

Along with most anti-slavery campaigners, Harriet was devastated by John Brown's death. But on the positive side, she saw that it had brought the injustice of slavery to the attention of many white Americans – and this gave Harriet hope that all slaves would soon be liberated. The night after Brown died, she talked it over with her family at supper.

'The time is coming for us,' she said. 'I know that God will answer our prayers.'

She went over to the window, and looked up at the North Star, shining bright in the sky.

'God put that star in the heavens to guide my way to freedom,' she said. 'It is proof that he wants us all to be free.'

* * *

In mourning for her brave friend, Harriet turned her attention back to fund raising, giving many more talks about her experiences on the Underground Railroad. Harriet's fame as a speaker brought her into contact with many rich and powerful abolitionists in white society, and in 1859, she was offered the lease of some property in Auburn, New York by politician and abolitionist William Seward.

Feeling safe in the protection of her influential white friends, Harriet was ready to defy the notorious 'Bloodhound Law'. She moved her frail parents and other family members back over the American border to live in her new property, while she carried on with her anti-slavery work.

The solid, two-storey house was a far cry from the drafty wooden cabin she had shared with her husband so many years ago in Dorchester County.

Harriet had not forgotten her promise to her mother to go back south for her younger sister. In 1860, she began another rescue attempt, but on arrival in Dorchester County, she was stopped in her tracks.

'It's too late, Harriet,' said a friend from the Underground Railroad. 'You began your journey before we could get word to you. Your poor sister Rachel got sick and died a few weeks ago.'

Harriet's thoughts flashed back to the baby sister she had minded when she was so little herself. It was hard to accept the fact that Rachel was gone for ever. Overcome with grief, Harriet tried to make contact with Rachel's two children in the hope they might be persuaded to escape in their mother's place. Through a mutual friend, she arranged to meet them in a forest close to the Brodess plantation. Harriet waited a whole night, hiding among the trees as a howling blizzard raged all around, but the pair never arrived. Harriet could only guess at their reasons – perhaps their escape plans had been thwarted at the last moment. It was too hazardous for Harriet to stay any longer in the area, so she moved on the next morning, her heart heavy in the knowledge that she would never see her nephew and niece again.

Determined to salvage something positive from this personal tragedy, Harriet heard about a slave family who wanted to escape north with their three small children. She decided to take this family with her, however the escape almost ended in disaster when Harriet knocked on the door of a familiar house, only to discover that her Underground Railroad contact no longer lived there.

A white man opened the door, staring at Harriet with eyes full of hate.

'If it's that good-for-nothing free black you're after, he was sold south for harbouring fugitives,' the man growled.

Harriet took a few steps backwards, thinking fast.

'We are lost and only wanted directions, sir,' she replied.

'Go to hell then!' shouted the man, slamming the door in her face.

Harriet hurried her small group away and led them through a swamp to a small, low-lying island, hidden in long, marshy grass. There, the fugitives waited, freezing cold, wet and hungry, watching slave patrols pass them by.

'That horrible brute back there must have raised the alarm,' Harriet said. The baby began whimpering softly. If he began to cry in earnest it would give them away to the slave catchers. Harriet handed his mother a bottle of sedative. 'A few drops of this should keep him quiet,' she whispered.

Harriet had to use all her hard-earned experience to bring the family to safety. The journey took much longer than usual, and was exhausting. By the time Harriet reached home, the stress had taken its toll and Harriet's health was shattered.

'You look awful,' Rit told her as she stood in the doorway of the new family home in Auburn, New York. Rit helped her daughter get to bed, then spent the next few months nursing her back to a full recovery.

'It's like you're Minty Ross again, that naughty child,' Rit said. 'Always getting into trouble.'

Harriet smiled despite herself. She was only thirty-eight years old, but she felt a lot older. This latest trip proved to be her last after ten long years on the Underground Railroad.

9

Civil War: 1861

'Do you have to leave again, Harriet?' pleaded Rit. 'Your father and I are not getting any younger, and it's not easy keeping this place going without you.' She sighed heavily, looking through the window at the spring blossom swaying on the trees outside.

Ben put his arm around Rit's shoulder.

'Hush now, my love, we've managed before, and we'll manage again. You know our Harriet always does the right thing. We've got to let her go.'

Harriet closed the lid of her battered suitcase and stood up to face her mother.

'I have to play my part in this war, Ma,' she said. 'Believe me, when the fighting is all over, slavery will be a thing of the past.'

It was April 1861. The tensions between the northern and southern states of America had finally reached breaking point. The northern states, known as the 'Union', stood for a united, free country, but the southern states, or the 'Confederacy' wanted to become independent of the North, keeping their old traditions of slavery. A week ago, Confederate guns had opened fire on Fort Sumter, a Union military base in South Carolina, forcing government troops to surrender. In response, President Abraham Lincoln had called for a volunteer Union Army to stop the South's rebellion – and with that, the American Civil War had begun.

Without a moment's hesitation, Harriet had decided to offer her services to the Union. She had packed a few essential possessions, and was leaving that morning for the train station, to head for the Union camps in South Carolina. Ben stepped forward to hug his daughter. For a split second, he was back in his old slave cabin in Dorchester County, bidding Harriet farewell before she fled to freedom.

'I shall miss you,' said Harriet, softly. 'But I can't sit back and do nothing.'

'I know, Harriet,' Ben replied. 'You'll never change. You can't let a good fight pass you by.'

Rit gave her daughter a kiss.

'Be careful, Harriet,' she said. 'Don't get carried away with all this war talk. We want you back in one piece.'

As Harriet boarded the train, a familiar feeling of excitement welled up inside her, tinged with the adrenaline rush of fear. It reminded her of how she always felt at the start of her Underground Railroad trips. She knew what she wanted to achieve, but she didn't know exactly how she would go about it.

I can make a difference, she said to herself. *There's no turning back now.*

Harriet watched the tobacco fields flash by as the train sped south. She thought about her meeting the day before with John Andrews, Governor of the state of Massachusetts. Her abolitionist fame had brought her into contact with some powerful people. The Governor's flattering words were still ringing in her head.

'You'll be a valuable asset to the Union,' he had told her. 'We need your skills and experience to help us fight this war.'

'Where should I go, sir?' Harriet had asked.

'Make your way to the Port Royal district in South

Carolina,' he answered. 'There are encampments there full of slaves who ran away when the fighting began. We call them 'contrabands', because they come from behind enemy lines.'

Harriet nodded, listening intently.

'We want you to organize the contrabands for us, both the men and women,' Governor Andrews went on. 'We need the men on our side so they can fight their old slave masters in the South. You can help persuade them to join us. They'll trust you, one of their own, more readily than they will ever trust us.'

'What about the women?' asked Harriet.

'Find them useful work, Mrs Tubman. We'll leave that to you to sort out.'

When Harriet arrived at the camps at Port Royal, there was more than enough work for her to do. She set up a laundry and showed the women how to earn money by cleaning soldiers' clothes and cooking food for the troops. Nurses were also urgently needed in the camp hospital. Harriet used her many abilities to both work as a nurse, and to train other women in practical nursing skills.

The first black regiment of the Civil War was led by a Union commander called General David Hunter.

When Harriet recruited hundreds of former slaves to join his regiment, an idea occurred to the General. He called Harriet to a meeting at his headquarters.

'Mrs Tubman, I understand that you have been a conductor on the Underground Railroad, and have experience of undercover travel,' he said.

'Yes, sir,' answered Harriet. 'I never ran a train off the track, and I never lost a passenger!' She was proud of this fact.

'I want you to use your experience to help us,' replied Hunter. He pointed to a large military map of the area that was pinned to a wall in his office.

'We need to know more about the terrain behind enemy lines,' he said. 'I want you to be a scout for us – take a small group of contraband with you to map all the local marshes and waterways. The information you gather will help us plan our secret operations.'

It was hard to think of a task better suited to Harriet's skills. The countryside in that part of South Carolina was not so different from the marshy terrain she was used to navigating on Maryland's Eastern Shore. Soon, Harriet knew the local land like the back of her hand. The information she passed on to General Hunter was of vital strategic use.

Harriet's reputation as a scout and a spy began to grow. In the summer of 1863, General Hunter decided to increase her responsibilities.

'We want to carry out a raid on the rice plantations along the Combahee River,' he told her, 'to destroy the enemy supply line and free hundreds of slaves in that area.' Harriet's eyes lit up; it sounded an exciting challenge.

'We need you to scout the area first,' he said. 'One of our best men, Colonel James Montgomery, will work with you.'

Harriet knew this name – before the war, Montgomery had worked with John Brown. Any friend of Brown's was a friend of hers.

'It will be a pleasure, sir,' she said.

Harriet and Colonel Montgomery got on well together. They decided that Harriet would lead three hundred men from the South Carolina Volunteers when the raid began. To prepare for the operation, Harriet went on nightly forays with her men to gather local intelligence.

'We've located all the enemy mines in the Combahee River!' Harriet told Montgomery one morning, on her return from a night-time spying mission. 'Our gunboats will be able to avoid them when they set off for the plantations.'

'Excellent work,' said Montgomery. 'Now we're all set to go.'

On the evening of June 1st 1863, the moon shone high in the sky over the fast moving waters of the Combahee River. It was the night of the raid. Harriet stood on the deck of the first gunboat as it steamed its way down river, while two other boats followed closely behind. As Harriet scanned the riverbanks, she recognized every rock and tree from her intelligence gathering expeditions.

The reconnaissance missions have paid off, she thought. *There will be no surprises for us tonight.*

The dark outlines of the enemy food stores came into view as the gunboat turned a bend in the river. All was quiet in the Confederate encampments – no one had raised the alarm to warn of an imminent attack. The tense silence was shattered as the three gunboats opened fire. Explosions ripped through the food stores, destroying the enemy's supplies, and huge fires broke out. Flames as tall as houses leaped up into the sky, casting an orange glow over the faces of all who watched anxiously from the boats.

Pandemonium errupted in the encampments all around.

We'll force them to surrender! thought Harriet, as she heard the cries of panic among the enemy troops on the riverbank. But she hadn't expected such utter disarray – the soldiers weren't prepared to fight, let alone surrender. Terrified, most of the Confederates simply turned on their heels and ran away.

Quick! We must get to the plantations… thought Harriet, remembering the plan she had agreed with General Montgomery. *If we can't capture or kill the enemy, at least we can free their slaves to fight for us!*

Holding up the Union flag, Harriet led her troops to the rice plantations, which were in a state of total chaos. The slaves could see from the burning food stores that an attack had taken place, but there was general confusion, and people did not know which way to run. With quiet authority, Harriet took charge of the situation.

'Follow us!' she cried, waving her flag. 'Union boats are waiting to take you away to freedom!'

A huge cheer rose up. The sight of this small, dignified black woman had a calming effect on the frightened crowds, winning their trust instantly.

Back at the riverbank, Harriet oversaw the evacuation of the plantation slaves on to the boats. The operation went smoothly, and she made sure that not a single slave was left behind. In total, over 750 slaves were freed during the raid – and most of them went on to join the Union army.

Back at headquarters in Port Royal, General Hunter was delighted at the success of the Combahee Raid.

'Congratulations, Mrs Tubman!' he said on her return, flashing Harriet a rare smile. News of the raid quickly spread to top levels of Union command, although official credit for the success was given to Colonel Montgomery. Despite this, the Union soldiers knew the truth – this had really been a victory for Harriet Tubman. It was an incredible achievement. Harriet was the first woman, black or white, ever to command a military raid in America.

Over the next two years, Harriet continued her work as a scout, a spy and a nurse. The army hospitals were always full of soldiers who were suffering from battle wounds, dysentery and other life-threatening illnesses caused by poor living conditions and dirty food and water. Harriet thought back to her childhood bouts of sickness, and remembered the herbal remedies that she had watched her mother prepare as she lay on her sickbed. Harriet put these memories to good use, by making natural medicines from local river plants.

If only Ma could see me now, thought Harriet one cold February morning in 1864, as she gave a sick soldier some of her home-made tonic. The young man smiled weakly.

'Thank you, Nurse,' he said. 'The men here say you're Mama Moses, who freed all those slaves before the war. Is it true?'

Harriet smiled. 'I'm just Nurse Tubman to you,' she said. 'What's your name, soldier?'

'Nelson,' came the reply. 'Nelson Davis.'

'Concentrate on getting well again, Nelson Davis,' said Harriet. 'We need strong men like you to win this war.'

* * *

The Civil War finally came to an end in April 1865, with victory for the Union. A few months before the fighting finally stopped, President Lincoln passed an amendment to the United States Constitution, banning slavery once and for all, right across the country. It was just as Harriet had promised her mother when she left to join the fight four years before – the war had brought freedom for everyone.

But despite the new constitution, America was still a divided country. Many white Americans were furious with President Lincoln for his part in abolishing slavery and refusing to allow the southern states to rule under their own laws. On April 14th 1865, just five days after the Civil War had officially ended, the President was shot dead at the hands of a white Confederate gang. Sadly, it seemed all was not well with the new United States of America.

Harriet was soon to experience this mood of resentment at first hand. On her train ride home from Virginia to New York State, she was not treated with the respect she deserved as a war veteran. As she sat patiently in her allocated seat, a conductor asked to see her ticket.

'This is not valid for your journey,' he said rudely. 'Go back where you belong, in the smoking car with the rest of your kind.'

Harriet refused to move. 'The army gave me this ticket for this seat, and I have earned my right to sit here,' she said quietly. 'I'm not going anywhere.'

The conductor tried to force Harriet to move, but he soon found that despite her small size, she was stronger than she looked.

'Guards!' he shouted. 'I need some help over here.'

It took three men to lift Harriet, kicking and struggling, out of the carriage and to throw her into the smoking car with the other black passengers. She landed awkwardly, but the humiliation was far worse than the sharp stab of pain.

'You've broken my arm!' she cried. 'In four years of war, this is the worst injury I've ever received.'

The conductor laughed, baring a row of rotten teeth.

'Welcome to peacetime,' he snorted, and walked away.

Harriet was shaking with anger. *Slavery may be dead and buried*, she thought. *But prejudice is clearly alive and well.*

10

Last Resort: 1873

It was already beginning to get dark as Harriet set off along the rough track that led to the isolated meeting place. Her bag was heavy with the money she had borrowed that afternoon from one of her rich white friends.

'Do you really need this much cash, Harriet?' her friend had asked, looking concerned. 'I trust you completely, my dear, but are you sure you can pay it all back?'

'Absolutely,' said Harriet. 'You are very kind to lend me this great sum. I will be able to give you back every dime, with interest.'

In all her fifty-one years, Harriet had never seen that much money. Two thousand dollars was a lot of cash, even when times were good. But times were not good, and Harriet had very little to live on.

She was finding it hard to scrape together the funds to feed herself and her immediate family, let alone all the people who visited her home in desperate circumstances, begging for her help as a last resort.

This plan will work, Harriet told herself, as she trudged along the stony road towards the forest. *Soon all my money worries will be over.*

Since the Civil War had ended eight years before, Harriet's financial problems had increased with every year that passed. Although Harriet earned some cash from odd jobs, raising livestock on her smallholding and renting out rooms in her house in Auburn, there was never enough money coming in. And in all these years, she had still not received any payment for her years of service during the war.

Poor Nelson is sick again, thought Harriet. *Soon we'll have another doctor's bill for his medicine.*

This was one of Harriet's greatest concerns. Nelson Davis, her second husband, was suffering from tuberculosis, a serious lung disease.

Harriet and Nelson had first met in hospital during the war. Nelson had been badly wounded, and Harriet had nursed him back to health.

At the end of the war, a few months after she had returned home, Nelson had turned up unexpectedly on her doorstep.

'Remember me?' he had asked when she opened the door. Harriet had a good memory for names.

'Why yes,' she had replied. 'It's Nelson Davis, isn't it. You called me Mama Moses.'

'That's right,' he said. 'I heard you have a room to rent.'

'You are welcome to take it,' said Harriet, with a smile. 'We can swap war stories.'

She missed the action and excitement of the war, and liked to talk about it whenever she could.

'I'd like that,' said Nelson. 'It's good to see you again, Nurse Tubman.'

'I'm glad you made it through the war,' said Harriet. She realized that she really meant it.

A year later, Harriet heard some bad news from a friend in Maryland. Her husband John had been shot dead by a white man in a roadside argument. Harriet was greatly upset by the injustice of the situation, because the white man was found 'not guilty' of murder, even though there was a witness to the crime. Yet she did not weep for John himself.

She had stopped grieving for her estranged husband many years before.

Her attention had turned to her new friend Nelson Davis.

He's much younger than me, she said to herself. *But we get on so well! It is like we have always known each other.*

One day, Nelson put Harriet's feelings into words.

'Harriet, we're good for each other,' he said. 'Now you're free again – would you ever consider marrying me?'

So in 1869, at the age of forty-seven, Harriet had married the twenty-five-year-old Nelson Davis. Ben and Rit were overjoyed to see their daughter settled and happy at last. But great sadness lay just around the corner. Two years after Harriet's wedding, her father became sick and died. He was in his late eighties, so his death was no great surprise; even so, Harriet missed him terribly. Her money problems, always bad up until then, got worse. Two years later, she and Nelson fell into serious debt, and their money difficulties spiralled out of control.

This was when Harriet came up with a money-making scheme. She had heard that gold bars were a good investment, and could be sold for a profit as the price of gold increased. She made inquiries, and was put in contact with a gold dealer.

'You'll make a handsome profit if you buy my gold with cash,' the dealer encouraged her.

They arranged a meeting place for Harriet to hand over two thousand dollars, in exchange for a stash of gold bars. This was where Harriet was heading now.

The forest was dark as Harriet reached the designated drop-off spot.

'Is anybody there?' she called. A cold wind picked up, rustling the leaves in the trees. A twig snapped behind her, and Harriet swung round.

Perhaps this wasn't such a good idea, she panicked. *I think I'd better go home.*

A heavy blow to her head knocked Harriet off her feet. The last thing she remembered was the sound of laughter.

When Harriet came to, light was creeping back into the forest. A new day was dawning. The bag of cash was nowhere to be seen – and of course there were no gold bars.

I've been tricked, thought Harriet miserably.

The realisation was far more painful than her splitting headache.

News spread of the incident, and public opinion was divided. 'Harriet Tubman is a war hero,' some people said. 'After everything she has done for us, we should feel sorry for her.' Donations of money poured in, paying off Harriet's debts.

But other people were not so kind. 'Only a fool could be duped in this way,' they muttered.

As ever, Harriet's sheer appetite for life pulled her through. A year later, in 1874, she and Nelson adopted a baby girl called Gertie. Harriet had to pinch herself to believe the truth – she finally had a child of her own! She was rushed off her feet caring for her baby daughter, her aging mother and her sickly husband. But for Harriet, spending every day with the people she loved the most was a blessing.

Rit survived Ben by nine years, dying of old age in 1880, and eight years later Harriet's husband Nelson lost his long battle with tuberculosis. He was just forty-five years old.

Harriet's life was changing. She was sixty-seven, with no parents or a husband to care for any more. Her daughter Gertie was now in her teens, almost an independent woman.

It was time for Harriet to find a new challenge. Looking at her daughter, and the limitations of a young girl's life, Harriet took up the cause of women's rights, and in particular, the rights of black women.

Harriet made frequent visits to New York, Boston and Washington DC to speak in favour of women's right to vote, giving examples of women's bravery during the Civil War to show they deserved equal rights to men.

'You're always so busy!' said Gertie, as Harriet left one morning for New York, to give a speech at a suffrage convention.

'There's so much still to be done,' replied Harriet, smiling at her daughter. 'Women should be allowed to vote. I may not see it in my lifetime, but I pray that you will.'

* * *

'Mother, the postman has delivered a package for you!'

Gertie was standing by the front door, holding a wooden box.

'It's come all the way from England!'

Gertie was now in her twenties, and married with a baby. But she still got as excited as a child when there were presents to open.

It took Harriet a while to come down the stairs. She was seventy-five years old, and not as quick as she once was.

'Who do you think it's from?' asked Gertie. Harriet shrugged.

'Let's open it and see,' she replied.

A few weeks before, Harriet had received a very special invitation from the Queen of England, Queen Victoria. It was the Diamond Jubilee, and Harriet had been invited to a celebration in England to mark the event. Clearly, Harriet's fame had spread far beyond American shores. There was no way Harriet could make such a long and expensive journey, so she had sent her apologies to the Queen.

'Open it, Mother!' cried Gertie, more excited than Harriet. Fumbling with the wrappings, Harriet pulled out a beautiful lace shawl and a silver medal. They were presents from the Queen.

Harriet gave her daughter a hug.

'This is a lovely surprise,' she said. 'But nothing is more precious to me than my family and the freedom we share,' she said. 'Not even a royal gift.'

Harriet remained active for another fourteen years, always helping others and campaigning for equal rights for women and all former slaves. In 1911, in her late eighties and confined to a wheelchair, she finally moved into a home for old, sick and homeless African Americans.

'Fancy living in a place that is named after you!' joked Gertie. Just a few years earlier, Harriet had given some of her land away to the church, so the Harriet Tubman Home for the Elderly could be built.

On March 10th 1913, Gertie was called urgently to the home. She was greeted at the door by an anxious doctor.

'I'm afraid your mother is very sick,' he said. 'She has acute pneumonia, and is slipping away from us.'

Gertie ran into Harriet's room. Her mother looked tiny and frail, propped up against a mountain of pillows. But she still had a smile for her daughter.

'My time is coming,' she whispered. Gertie held Harriet's hand.

'Don't leave me...' she said to her mother.

How many times have I heard those words? thought Harriet. She felt sad. This time, she knew she would not be coming back for anyone.

Evening drew in, and Harriet's room filled up with her closest friends and family. Gertie did not turn anyone away – Harriet would not have wanted that. As the sun set on the cold spring day and the room grew dark, Harriet woke up from her sleep. As always, she was thinking of those around her.

'I'm going to heaven now,' she said. 'I'll prepare a place there for you all.'

Then she closed her eyes for the last time.

Post Script

On March 13th 1913, Harriet was buried with military honours at Fort Hill Cemetery in Auburn, New York. She was buried next to her dear brother Henry, who had died the year before. Her medal from Queen Victoria was placed inside her coffin, which was draped with an American flag. This was a perfect tribute to the incredible journey Harriet had made during her lifetime, from rebellious slave to national and international hero.

Also available...

Cholera can kill thousands of people in a single outbreak. It's unstoppable. Or so people think. Dr John Snow knows the real cause of cholera – *and* how to stop it. But first, he will have to convince doctors, governments and the public that everything they know about cholera is wrong.

Real Lives are narrative accounts of the life and times of some of the world's most iconic figures.

ISBN: 978-1-4081-7840-9
RRP: £5.99

1
Cholera

1832, Killingworth, near Newcastle-Upon-Tyne

'Mr Snow, come quick – it's me sister!'

The boy was hurtling down the main road of Killingworth village. His voice echoed off the grey stone buildings and leaked up and out into the dusk, dissolving into an evening that was already filled with despair.

John Snow could hear the urgency in the boy's cries. He picked up his medical bag quickly, but with a heavy heart. It was only his third day in the village, but he had already attended several patients with the disease that everyone was dreading.

'It's the cholera, I know it is. Please, can you come and see, can you help us?' The boy, about nine years old, stood in front of John, bent over, hands on his knees, the words forced out between his panting breaths.

John recognized the boy; the previous day, he had tended to the boy's father, whom he had diagnosed with cholera – and who had since suffered a painful and tormented death. 'Let's go,' he said with an upward nod, and the two of them walked briskly side by side back up the main street, without saying a word.

It was August 1832. John Snow was only nineteen years old, an apprentice doctor who was tending single-handedly to the five hundred or so inhabitants of the coal-mining village of Killingworth. His master, William Hardcastle, was back in Newcastle upon Tyne, about six miles to the south, where cholera had already claimed hundreds of lives in the past year. The disease had stalled in February, but it had recently begun claiming lives once again, in Newcastle and in Killingworth – so Hardcastle had had no choice but to send John to Killingworth on his own.

There had been nine cases of cholera in Killingworth in January and February, five of them fatal. John was determined to give people the best care and treatment he could, to minimise the number of cases now that the disease had returned there.

They turned off the high street, still walking at a brisk pace. John and the boy both flinched when they heard an explosion at the coal mine; using gunpowder to loosen the coal from the coalface had become common practice in the past few years. John pictured the people working in the mine – boys as young as five dragging and pushing trucks loaded with coal up through cramped tunnels; men hacking at the coalface or shovelling up loosened coal from the floor. Workers typically stayed in the mine for ten hours at a time, not even coming to the surface to go to the toilet – despite the fact that of course there were no lavatories inside the mine.

Stepping into the house, John saw the boy's younger sister laid out on a bed next to the fireplace. The dim flickering of firelight and candlelight made the little girl's gaunt face look even more ghastly. Her eyes were shadowed and deep-set, her skin wrinkled like a prune, her face in a tortured spasm. All the signs were there – this was cholera, without question.